Be Bold

Be Brave

Be Yourself

A Journal

Susan Lute

Be Bold, Be Brave, Be Yourself

Susan Lute

Crazy Hair Publishing
Portland, Oregon
www.susanlute.com

For everything there is a season. In
the perennial garden of summer
blooms potential.
This book is dedicated to you.
In these pages tell your story.

Date_____Page____

_____Date_____Page___

_____Date_____Page____

Date_____Page____

Date_____Page_____

_____Date_____Page___

Date_____Page____

_____Date_____Page___

Date_____ Page_____

_____Date_____Page___

Date_____Page___

Date_____Page____

Date_____Page____

Date_____Page____

_____Date_____Page___

_____Date_____Page___

_____Date_____Page____

Date_____Page___

Date_____ Page____

Date_____Page___

_____Date_____Page___

_____Date_____Page____

Date_____Page_____

Date_____Page___

_____Date_____Page____

Date_____Page____

Date_____ Page____

Date_____Page____

_____Date_____Page___

_____Date_____Page___

Date_____Page___

Date_____Page_____

Date_____Page____

_____Date_____Page____

Date_____Page____

Date_____Page___

Date_____ Page____

Date_____ Page____

Date_____Page___

Date_____ Page____

Date_____ Page___

Date_____Page____

Date_____Page___

_____Date_____Page____

Date_____Page____

_____Date_____Page___

Date_____ Page____

Date_____ Page____

Date_____Page____

Date_____Page___

Date_____Page_____

Date_____Page____

_____Date_____Page___

Made in the USA
Las Vegas, NV
01 March 2022

44843891R00066